Asian Favourite Stories

SINGAPORE

Text by

Leon Comber

Illustrations

Beryl Kwok

TALISMAN

First published in Southeast Asia in 2011
by Talisman Publishing Pte Ltd

52 Genting Lane #06-05
Rubyland Complex 1
Singapore 349560
t: +65 6749 3551
f: +65 6749 3552
www.talismanpublishing.com

Design
Norreha Sayuti
Hazel Concha

Acknowledgements
*The author is grateful for the suggestions and help provided by
Lee Su Yin in preparing the stories.*

ISBN: 978-981-08-6955-7

Contents

How Singapore got its Name 4

Kusu Island 8

You Cannot Please Everyone 12

How Bukit Merah got its Name 14

How the Mousedeer Cheated the Tiger 18

Singapore: A Great City 21

Steamships Come to Singapore 24

A Javanese Princess in Singapore 27

Badang — The Famous Strongman
of Singapore 32

Singapore Invaded by Rats 36

The Legend of Junk Island 39

The Pirates of Riau 44

Glossary 49

How Singapore got its Name

Long long ago there was a king of Sumatra who was a famous hunter. His name was Sang Nila Utama. He visited the Riau Islands to hunt with some of his men.

Suddenly, he saw a large deer in front of him. "Shoot it!" he shouted to his men. But, although they shot arrows and threw spears at it, it escaped. The king chased it to the top of a high hill. He was quite out of breath. He could not see the deer anywhere. But in front of him, not far, was a beautiful island with a beach of golden sand.

"What's the name of that place?" the king asked his officers.

"Tumasek," they replied.

"Let us go there," he said.

When they were about to reach Tumasek, the sky became dark and it started to rain heavily. There was a strong wind and the sea became rough. The king and his men were afraid that their boat would sink.

"Your Majesty," said one of his senior officers, "let us throw everything we can into the sea."

They even wanted to throw the king's golden crown into the water. "No!" he ordered. "That must always remain with me. Wherever I put down my crown, is my kingdom."

But the storm became fiercer and fiercer. The waves were higher than the ship itself.

The king's officers cried, "Your Majesty, unless we throw your crown overboard, the ship will sink and we shall all drown."

Sang Nila Utama took his crown off his head, looked at it for the last time, and threw it into the sea.

Immediately, the thunder and lightning stopped and the wind dropped. The waves became calm and the boat reached the shore.

After resting for some time, the king and his officers felt better. They had some food and drink and went hunting in the forest. Just then, the king saw a strange animal running through the trees. He had never seen an animal like it before. It had a black head, a white neck, and a red body. "What is it?" he asked his men.

"A lion, Your Majesty."

"It doesn't look like a lion to me," Sang Nila Utama said. "But it is a good sign. Let's move our capital here. I like this place."

"What name shall we give it?" his officers asked.

"Singapura," the king replied. "In our language, it means 'lion city'."

Kusu Island

Many years ago, a Chinese fisherman and a Malay fisherman lived in a village on the island of Singapura, which has now become the great city of Singapore. They were good friends and they were so poor that they both had to go out to sea every day to catch fish to sell in the market. The Chinese was called Ah Yam and the Malay Syed Rahman.

One day, although the weather was bad and there was a fierce storm with thunder and lightning, Ah Yam went out to sea. His wife asked him not to do so but he did not listen to her. The rough sea and the strong wind made it difficult for him to fish, and his little boat rocked from side to side. While he was trying to pull up his fishing net from the sea, Ah Yam slipped and fell into the sea. He went down, down under the waves and he felt he would never come up again. When he did, he could hardly breathe because his mouth and nose were filled with water, but he managed to scream, "Please help me. I am drowning. Who will look after my wife and children?"

When he was about to give up hope, a large turtle appeared and swam towards him. It was the biggest turtle he had ever seen in his life. "Climb on to my back and hold tight," the turtle told him. "I shall take you to shore." The fisherman did as he was told, and the turtle took him to a nearby island where he climbed off the turtle's back on to the sandy beach. "Thank you, Mr. Turtle," he said, "for saving my life," but the turtle was already swimming far away although he looked back and waved his flipper at Ah Yam. Ah Yam looked and looked but he could not see Singapura, and after some time he decided to make the island his home. He built a hut and found a fresh-water stream and was able to live quite well as he found many fresh fruits on the island.

One day, when there was a heavy storm, he heard someone crying, "Help! Help me! I am drowning". He thought he recognized the voice. It was his old Malay friend, Syed Rahman, who was being carried to the island on the back of Mr. Turtle, the same turtle that had helped him. "My dear friend," Ah Yam greeted him, "how pleased I am to see you." The two men told each other their stories. Syed Rahman had been caught in a fierce storm, too, and his boat had sunk. By this time, Mr. Turtle was swimming away and although they called out to him to come back so that they could thank him for saving their lives, he soon disappeared from sight.

As they could see no way of returning home, the two friends lived happily together and spent their time hunting for animals and fish.

To thank the turtle for saving their lives, they built a Chinese temple on a small hill overlooking the sea, a Malay shrine, and a statue of Mr. Turtle, all of which can still be found on the island which is now known as Kusu Island. "Ku" is the Hokkien word for "turtle" and "su" is the Hokkien word for "island". The temple has an image of Toh Peh Kong in it, looking like an elderly Chinese gentleman with a white beard and red cheeks, who is believed to look after the interests of the Chinese and save them from danger. The Malay shrine is considered a holy place, too, by both Malays and Chinese as Syed Rahman, and his mother and sister, who are considered very holy women, are buried there. Today, thousands of people visit Kusu Island each year by ferry from Singapore to pray at the Chinese temple and Malay shrine which are gaily decorated with flags and banners.

You Cannot Please Everyone

Many years ago, a Chinese farmer and his son were leading a buffalo to the market in Singapore. Someone who saw them pass by called out to the farmer, "Why don't you ride?" The man thought this was a good idea and sat on the buffalo. His son continued walking by his side.

Soon they passed an old woman who was planting rice. She called out to the farmer, "Why are you so lazy? You are a big, strong man. Why don't you walk and let your son ride instead?"

The man replied, "I am not lazy! Very well, I shall let my son ride." The farmer got down from the buffalo and told his son to sit on it.

Just before they reached the market, an old man working in the fields called out to them, "It is not right for a boy to ride while his father walks."

The farmer then sat on the buffalo behind his son. They had not gone very far, when someone else called out to them, "Why are you so cruel? How can a poor buffalo carry two persons? You should be ashamed."

On hearing this, both the farmer and his son jumped off the buffalo. They cut off some branches from a tree and tied the buffalo's feet to it so that they could carry the buffalo supported between the branches.

When they entered the market, some children called out laughingly to them, "How can you carry a buffalo? The buffalo should carry you."

The buffalo became frightened at the noise, and was able to set itself free. It ran away as fast as it could, and the farmer and his son never saw it again.

As they started to walk home, the farmer said to his son, "Well, we've lost our buffalo but we have learned a good lesson today. You can never hope to please everyone, no matter how hard you try."

How Bukit Merah got its Name

Long, long ago, some fishermen were fishing in the Singapore harbour not far from shore. Suddenly, the colour of the sea changed from blue to silver. The fishermen were surprised as they could not understand what had happened. Suddenly, one of them shouted a warning, "Look out! We are being attacked by swordfish!" As they looked around, they saw that the sea was swarming with swordfish who were heading straight for them.

Some of the swordfish leapt out of the water, and attacked the helpless fishermen. The fishermen had no weapons to fight back and several of them were killed.

The fishermen sailed for shore as quickly as they could and reported what had happened to Paduka Sri Maharaja, the king of Singapore. He was a noble and fine man, and he listened carefully to what they said.

He replied, "If the swordfish dare come any closer, I shall order our army to form a wall with their shields and attack them with their swords." Not many days afterwards, as it happened, the swordfish attacked again and this time they headed straight for the shore. As the king had promised, his soldiers were waiting for them with their shields held in front of them to form a wall and their swords held in their hands. But the swordfish were strong enough to cut through the shields as if they were made of paper and stab the soldiers' legs. The soldiers howled in pain and quickly retreated to a nearby hill. Fortunately, the swordfish did not follow them. The king's doctors bandaged their wounds and gave them some medicine. The blood from their wounds flooded the ground and the hill became red, and thereafter, to this day in modern Singapore, it is called 'Bukit Merah' or 'Red Hill'.

The king, quite naturally, was not very happy at what had happened and he said that he would give a large reward to anyone who could help him defeat the swordfish.

One young boy, called Hang Nadim, came forward. He explained to the king what he wanted him to do. "Your Majesty," he said, "instead of your soldiers using shields, use banana trees instead. When the swordfish attack, their sharp noses will become stuck in the banana trees, and your soldiers can easily kill them." The next time the swordfish attacked Singapore, the boy's plan

was used and it succeeded. The swordfish did not dare attack Singapore after that.

The king was very pleased with Hang Nadim and rewarded him with several bars of gold. The victory over the swordfish was celebrated with a big feast.

How the Mousedeer Cheated the Tiger

This is a Malay story told in Singapore.

Many, many years ago in Singapore there was a fierce tiger. It was very angry with a mouse-deer who annoyed him, and as he was a fierce tiger, he wanted to teach him a good lesson and eat him.

The mouse-deer told this to his good friend, Mr. Snake.

"Don't worry," Mr. Snake said. "I can help you. Please listen carefully to what I tell you to do."

So the mouse-deer waited near some bamboos. After some time, the tiger came and asked him angrily what he was doing. "I'm guarding the sultan's flute," the mouse-deer answered. He showed the tiger a hole in one of the bamboos.

"How do you play it?"

"With your tongue," said the mouse-deer.

"May I play it?" asked the tiger.

"Of course," replied the mouse-deer. "But I must first go away for the sultan will be very angry with me if he knows that I've allowed you to play it."

The tiger poked his tongue into the hole. The edges of the hole were very sharp and the tip of his tongue was cut off. (That is why to this day tigers have short tongues). He roared with pain and chased after the mouse-deer who managed to escape.

The tiger saw the mouse-deer waiting for him in front of a nest of wild bees.

"Aha, don't think you can escape from me this time," he said. "Although I've lost the tip of my tongue, I still have sharp teeth and can eat you."

"Please wait a moment, Mr. Tiger," replied the clever mouse-deer. "I'm now guarding the sultan's gong. Wouldn't you like to strike it before you have your dinner?"

"What a good idea! Someone once told me that rich people always strike a gong before eating dinner."

"Well, please do that before you eat me, Mr. Tiger," said the mouse-deer.

The tiger hit the wild bees' nest with his paw. All the bees came swarming out and bit the tiger on the nose. The tiger hopped up and down in pain. His eyes watered so much that he could hardly see.

The mouse-deer then ran off and waited for the tiger in front of his friend, Mr. Snake, who was sleeping.

"Ho, ho!" the tiger growled. "You really think you are very clever, don't you? I'll teach you a good lesson now."

"Just wait a moment," the mouse-deer said. "I am guarding the sultan's turban. Whoever wears it can become sultan. Would you like to try it on?"

The tiger touched the snake with his paw. Mr. Snake woke up and bit the tiger. The tiger gave a great shout and run away. He never troubled the mouse-deer again.

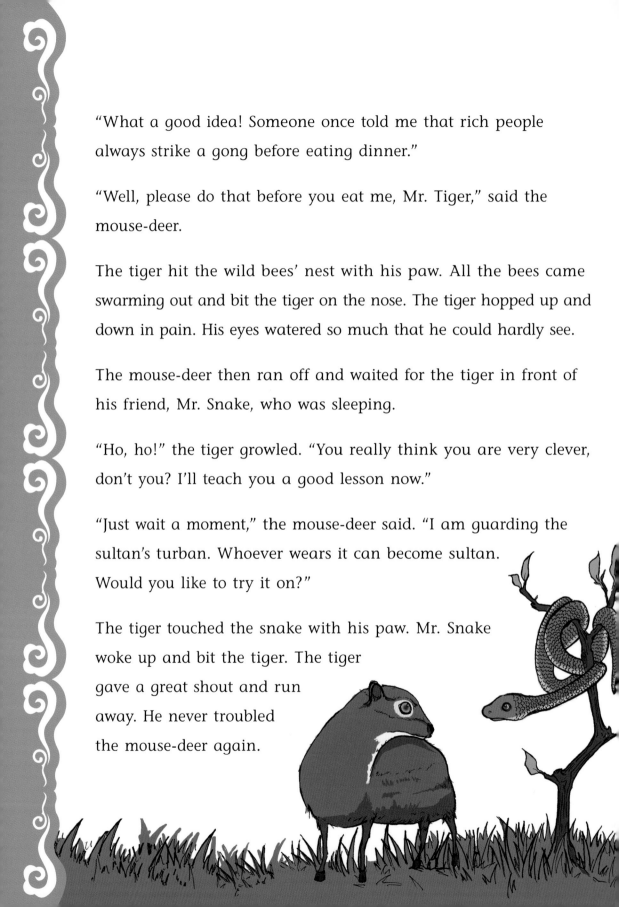

Singapore: A Great City

Did you know that Singapore has twice been a great city?

Long, long ago, it was believed that Indonesian and Malay kings fought to establish it. Then later, Sir Stamford Raffles, who worked for the British East India Company and made an agreement with a Malay ruler for the British to govern Singapore, also helped.

Even now, there is a statue of Raffles in front of the Victoria Memorial Hall.

After Singapore became independent, it became one of the most important ports in the world. You can see ships in its harbour from all over the world. But did you know that the Americans helped to develop Singapore, too?

A long time ago, in 1834, an American named Joseph Balestier came to live in Singapore. He was the representative of the American government. He became very well known and popular, and he helped many people, most of them Chinese, to start plantations in Singapore for growing pepper and other spices. He asked the government to pass a law allowing them to keep the land on which they had built their plantations after working hard on them.

Planting became important in those days. Joseph Balestier himself started growing sugar cane. He cleared the jungle at Serangoon, some miles out of the centre of Singapore, and made a plantation there.

The fields were ploughed by oxen and an elephant. Joseph Balestier was very clever. He dug a ditch around each field to drain away the rain water into a wide canal which ran through the plantation to the sea. After cutting the sugar cane, it was loaded into small boats which floated down the canal to his factory, where it was made ready for sale. Joseph Balestier lived in a beautiful house near the factory. It was surrounded by all kinds of beautiful flowers and plants that he had brought in from many countries.

Joseph Balestier's wife brought a large bell from America. She gave it to St. Andrew's Cathedral where it was placed in the new spire that was being built, and its chimes could be heard all over Singapore. The bell is now in Singapore's National Museum.

Joseph Balestier's house and plantation have disappeared a long time ago. But it is not difficult to find the place where they were for the road that ran alongside them is now named Balestier Road.

Steamships Come to Singapore

When the first steamship came to Singapore more than two hundred years ago, hundreds of people came to watch it when it steamed into the harbour. It was a strange-looking ship with smoke pouring out of its funnel. It was the first time people had seen a ship that could travel without sails. Many people were frightened, "It is a monster!" they cried, "How can it travel without sails. Don't let it enter the harbour!" But there was nothing they could do about it.

The ship came steadily on, churning up water as its steam engine pushed the ship through the sea. But gradually people became used to seeing steamships and they were no longer afraid.

At first, steamships anchored in the harbour, and their cargo was carried into the Singapore River by small boats, called sampans. It took a long time before the ships were unloaded and new cargoes loaded, and the ships' captains did not like the delay. They said they lost money because of the delay when their ships were being unloaded and loaded with fresh cargo. Then a new harbour was found. It was about three miles south of Singapore through a narrow gap between the south of Singapore and the two small islands of Pulau Brani and Pulau Blakang Mati, now known as Sentosa. The water was deeper here and ships could come close to the shore without touching the bottom. It was a wild place.

The land was surrounded by jungle with wild animals such as tigers, pigs and deer living in it. The first ships to use the new harbour were ships of the British steamship company, the P & O Line. The P & O Company bought some land from the Malay prince who owned it, and built a wharf, a coal shed, and some offices. Their ships then steamed directly into the new harbour and were able to anchor alongside the wharf. They could load and unload their cargo much more quickly. The new harbour was made bigger and merchants built wharves and warehouses there. Gradually the new harbour became well-known as a centre for steamers travelling between Europe, Singapore and other Eastern ports.

The coming of the steamships changed the old ways of trading in Singapore. The old sailing ships had to rely on the monsoon winds to sail to and from Singapore. In those days, when Chinese junks came to Singapore from China, they sailed with the northeast monsoon winds, and they had to wait many months in Singapore before the monsoon winds changed direction and enabled them to sail back to China. Steamships did not have to wait for the monsoon winds as their steam engines enabled them to travel regularly from port to port carrying both cargo and passengers.

A Javanese Princess in Singapore

Did you know that a Javanese princess is buried at Mount Faber Road, near the junction with Telok Blangah Road? Please go to see her shrine if you have not seen it. There is an interesting story connected with her. It is the story of Radin Mas Ayu, a beautiful Javanese princess, who lived many hundreds of years ago.

A long, long time ago, a young man called Pangeran Adipati Agung lived in Java with his brother, who was the Sultan. Pangeran fell in love with a beautiful dancer, who often danced at his brother's palace. Although Pangeran asked his brother for permission to marry her, his brother refused. "I forbid you to marry her," his brother said, "She is only a dancer and not from a royal family."

However, Pangeran did not listen to his brother, and secretly married the dancer, whom he loved very much. In due course, they had a daughter, whom they named Radin Mas Ayu. Everyone marveled at her beauty. She was just as beautiful as her mother.

The sultan was very angry when he found out that his brother has disobeyed him. He asked his advisers what he should do. "Your Majesty," they replied, "why not send your brother Pangeran away to attack a neighbouring country? While he is away, we can punish him by burning down his house."

The sultan thought a long time about this before deciding to follow their advice. Pangeran's house was set on fire while his wife was inside. Although she screamed for help, no one helped her and she was killed in the flames, though her daughter was saved by a faithful servant.

When Pangeran returned to Java, and found out what had happened, he vowed he would never again have anything to do with his brother, and he and his daughter sailed for Singapore. He built a house and lived at Telok Blangah. They lived happily there for several years until one day the village was attacked by pirates from Riau. Pangeran fought bravely against the pirates and drove them off. The Sultan of Singapore was grateful for Pangeran's help and asked him to join his court. When the sultan discovered that Pangeran came from a royal family, he decided to give his daughter in marriage to him, as Pangeran had been living alone since his wife died.

The next year, Pangeran and the sultan's daughter had a son whom they named Tengku Chik. But Pangeran's wife became jealous of her husband's love for his daughter, and she decided to teach him a good lesson. She then asked her nephew, Tengku Bagus, to help her. Although "Bagus" in Malay means "good", Tengku Bagus was an evil man who had long wanted to marry Pangeran's daughter. "Leave it to me," he said to Pangeran's wife. "I know what to do".

On a dark night, not long afterwards, he and his men broke into Pangeran's house and seized him. They tied his hands and feet and lowered him into a well where they left him to die.

Tengku Bagus reported to Pangeran's wife what he had done. "I am very glad," she said, "You have done what I wanted you to do.

Is there anything I can do for you?" This was the chance that Tengku Bagus had been waiting for. "Auntie," he said. "I have long wanted to marry Radin Mas Ayu. If you can arrange this, I shall always be grateful to you."

Pengeran's wife forced Radin Mas Ayu to agree to marry Tengku Bagus. On the day of the wedding, Radin Mas Ayu was asked whether she had obtained her father's permission to marry Tengku Bagus. Radin Mas Ayu did not know what to say, but her step-brother, Tengku Chik, spoke up. "No," he said, "She doesn't have her father's permission. But we can obtain his permission. I know where he is." Then he led the group to the well where Pangeran was imprisoned, and in no time Pangeran was pulled out alive from the well. Tengku Bagus, who had been watching anxiously what was going on, as soon as he saw that Pangeran had been released, tried to stab him with his keris. However, Radin Mas Ayu, protected her father by standing in front of him, and she was accidentally stabbed and died in her father's arms.

When Pangeran's followers saw what had happened they seized Tengku Bagus and tied his arms behind. "Let's throw him into the well," they shouted, "as he did to Pangeran". But Pangeran said in a firm voice, "No! Keep him tied up but let's take him to court to be tried by a judge and sentenced." In the confusion that followed, Pangeran's wicked wife seized the chance to escape. She

had not gone very far, when the sky turned dark, and it began to rain, and there were loud clashes of thunder and dazzling flashes of lightning. She continued to run through the forest but she was struck by lightning and killed. No one was sorry for her as they felt she had been punished for her wickedness.

Radin Mas Ayu, who had given her life for her father, was buried in Telok Blangah where she had lived with her father, at the foot of present-day Mount Faber, which in those days was called Telok Blangah Hill.

Badang — The Famous Strongman of Singapore

About seven hundred years ago, a poor young man named Badang lived on the banks of the Singapore River. He was thin and weak but he dreamed of becoming big and strong. He liked to fish in the river. He cast his fish nets along the bottom of the river every evening and collected the fish the next morning. One morning he saw there were only fish heads and bones in the net. He could not understand what had happened but he took the fish net home and cleaned and dried it ready for the evening. That evening, he cast his fish net on the bottom of the river. When he went to pull up the net the next morning, it felt very light. He saw there were only fish bones in it. He felt very angry, and he decided to sleep on the river-bank that night to find out what was going on. He took a small log of wood for his pillow, a mat to sleep on, and an old sarung to cover himself. He also took a keris to protect himself. The fresh air and the movement of the water in the river, made him feel very sleepy and he soon fell asleep. He dreamt that was very strong and could lift a fully loaded sampan. Then he dreamt that he lifted a huge rock which he found by the side of the river, and was able to throw it into the air. The rock flew through the air and landed far away at the mouth of the river. In his dream, Badang became very rich and strong. Suddenly a giant appeared before him. "Who are you?" Badang cried out. But the giant smiled. He did not answer but he vomited two red gems. "Swallow these two precious stones," he told Badang, "and you will become very strong and famous."

Badang then woke up. He found that he had become very strong and could easily lift very heavy weights. He still worked as a fisherman, and as he was so strong, he was able to collect every day very large quantities of fish in his net.

One day, he saw a group of men trying to push a heavy boat into the river. They tried and tried and still they could not make the boat move. Badang offered to help then. "How can you help us?" they asked. "You look very small and weak." "Well, I may look like that," answered Badang, "but actually I am very strong. Why don't you let me try?" By this time, there were hundreds of men trying to move the boat.

This came to the notice of Seri Rama Wira Kerma, the King of Tumasek, as Singapore was called in those long-ago days, who came to the river to see what was happening. "Do you really believe you are strong enough to move the boat?" he asked Badang. "Yes, your Majesty," Badang replied, and without saying any more he walked over to the boat and pushed it easily into the river. The King was so impressed that he summoned Badang to his court and made him commander-in-chief of the army.

By this time, Badang's fame had spread far and wide, and the Rajah of Kling in India told his strongest man, Wadi Bijaya, to go to Singapore to challenge Badang to a duel to see who was the stronger. Wadi Bijaya set sail with seven ships loaded with gold, silver, and precious stones. If Badang won the contest, the seven loaded ships would be given to the King of Tumasek but if Badang lost, the King of Tumasek would have to give seven ships loaded with the same amount of gold, silver, and precious stones to the Rajah of Kling. The two strong men fought with each other and Badang won all of the contests. The last match was to lift a huge rock that was at the mouth of the Singapore River. Badang was startled when he saw it because he recognized it was the same huge rock that he had thrown in his dream. Wadi Bijaya tried his best but he was unable to lift the rock but Badang picked it up and lifted it above his head with ease before putting it down again. This contest between the two strong men representing India and Tumasek brought great fame to Badang and Tumasek.

The rock that Badang lifted above his head is believed to be the old stone with some writing in an unknown language on it that was found at the mouth of the Singapore River in June 1819. You can still see a piece of this stone in the National Museum of Singapore.

Singapore Invaded by Rats

Did you know that Singapore was invaded by rats just over 200 years ago?

At that time, there were few wild or tame animals in Singapore but there were thousands and thousands of rats. No one knew where they came from but they were all over the island. Some of them were as large as cats and they were very fierce too. One night, someone heard a cat mewing. "Meow, meow," it sounded very pitiful. They went outside to see what was happening. There was a group of large rats attacking a poor cat that was unable to defend itself against so many rats. They were biting its paws, ears, tail, and nose, and the cat was crying out in pain. Everyone felt sorry for it. Someone fetched a stick and chased the rats away. They fled as fast as they could but the cat managed to catch two of them that had been biting its ears, and killed them. Someone took the injured cat to Colonel William Farquhar's house which was nearby. In 1819, Farquhar was in charge of Singapore when the British occupied it. He was well thought of by the people as he understood their customs and language, and he was known to be fair and considerate. "What have you got there?" he asked. "It's a cat that has been attacked and bitten by rats," they replied. Farquhar took pity on the cat and said that it could be left with him to look after.

What had happened made Farquhar think about what should be done to get rid of the thousands of rats that were causing so much trouble all over the island. There were rats in all the houses, including his own house. He soon issued a notice throughout Singapore: "Anyone who kills a rat and brings its dead body to me will be paid one wang." 'Wang' in Malay means 'money' but in those long-ago days it was the name of a small coin.

Many methods were used to kill rats, including setting traps to catch them, and putting down poison for them to eat. Others searched for rat holes and tried to force the rats to come out so that they could kill them. Every day crowds of people waited outside Farquhar's house with the rats they had killed to claim a reward. On some days, thousands of dead rats were brought in. In order to increase the number of rats killed, Farquhar increased the reward for each dead rat. In the end, there were so many dead rats brought in that Farquhar ordered a deep trench to be dug so that they could be buried in it. Gradually the number of rats began to grow less, and people were only bringing in ten or twenty dead rats a day. Finally the people of Singapore won the battle against the rats, and there was no more trouble.

the Legend of Junk Island

Many hundreds of years ago, Singapore was ruled by a rich and powerful king who lived on Bukit Larangan. Bukit Larangan in Malay means 'Forbidden Hill' but Bukit Larangan is now called 'Fort Canning'. The king was so powerful that he ruled not only the island of Singapore but many of the nearby small islands such as Pulau Tekong, Pulau Ubin, Pulau Hantu, Pulau Brani, and Pulau Jong. If you look at a map of Singapore, you can see these islands. This is the legend of one of them, Pulau Jong, which in Malay means 'Junk Island'.

Not many people lived on these islands in those long-ago days. Even nowadays not many people live there as they prefer to live on the main island of Singapore, which has now developed into a great international city and seaport.

In former times, the islands were used by pirates as hiding places from which they could attack ships sailing past. Sometimes they were brave enough to attack ships inside Singapore's harbour. One of the most feared pirates was called Azman, who commanded a large fleet of pirates. The king was determined to capture him and destroy his pirate gang but it was not easy as the pirates were well armed and very fierce. Many sea battles were fought between the king's men and the pirates but it was still not possible to defeat them. One of the king's wise men told him, "Your Majesty, the only way we can beat the pirates is to ask for the help of the friendly spirits who live under the sea. If we can get them to help us, I'm sure we can succeed." The king decided to do this, and he ordered the wise man to contact

the leader of the water spirits to ask for his help. Actually, the wise man did not know how to do this but he thought of a clever way. He wrote a letter to the king of the water spirits. "O leader of the water spirits, my king has asked me to contact you. We have never caused you any trouble and we have always lived in peace together. We would like to ask for your help in fighting the pirates, who are attacking ships whenever they sail nearby. The head of the pirates is a wicked man called Azman. They are evil men who attack ships, rob them of their cargo, and often kill the sailors and passengers. We are sure your honour will agree to support us in our fight against evil and help us to defeat Azman and his gang. If your honour agrees, please give us a sign."

The wise man folded the letter, placed it in an envelope which he weighed down with a stone, and dropped it into the sea. Nothing was heard for some time, until one day the king received news that a Chinese junk would be visiting Singapore on its way back from India to China. It was loaded with a cargo of precious goods that were a gift from the king of India to the ruler of China. "Let us show them that we are a friendly people," the king said, "and entertain the captain and crew of the junk to a grand feast while they are here." When the junk arrived, all arrangements for the feast were made, and the captain of the junk and his crew were welcomed and given a lavish feast which they enjoyed very much.

When the junk left Singapore for China some days afterwards, it was seen off by the king and his high officers. They noticed, however, that the sea had become unusually calm. "I think this is a good sign," the king said, "that they will have a safe voyage back to China." But the wise minister who had written the letter to the leader of the water spirits smiled, as he knew it was a sign from the water spirits that his letter had been received and the water spirits would support the king and his men in their fight against the pirates.

Soon afterwards, the king and his ministers heard the sound of cannon fire and although the junk was out of sight, they knew that the pirates must have attacked it. "Quick," said the king, "let us do what we can to help our friends fight the pirates."

He ordered his navy to leave as soon as possible to help the Chinese junk. As their ships approached the junk, they saw it was being attacked by the pirates, who had by then already boarded it and thrown the crew into the sea. Suddenly, however, the waves parted and a band of friendly spirits emerged from the sea. They were heavily armed and looked very warlike. With a great frightening shout, "Hurrah!" they attacked the pirates, seized hold of the junk, and turned it upside down into the sea.

The pirates were thrown into the sea with their leader, Azman. Many of them were drowned, and those that survived, including Azman, were hunted down by the king's men who shot arrows at them. Azman was wounded in the shoulder by an arrow and pulled out of the sea as they wanted to take him back to Singapore so that he could be tried for piracy.

The crew of the Chinese junk who had been thrown into the sea by the pirates were rescued and taken back to Singapore where they were allowed to live and settle down.

The junk sank to the bottom of the sea where it turned into an island which still stands to this day. It is called Pulau Jong or Junk Island.

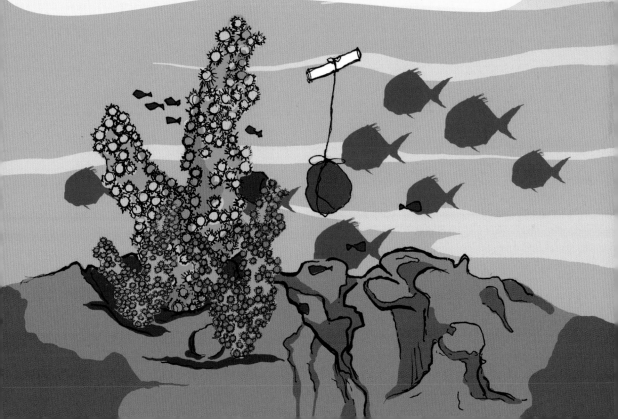

The Pirates of Riau

The Riau Islands are a group of small islands near Singapore. Over one hundred years ago, a group of pirates from Borneo decided to hide in the sea surrounding the islands. They attacked many ships sailing to and from Singapore and they caused a lot of trouble. Their chief was very fierce-looking. He was called Kerbau Hitam or Black Buffalo because he had very dark skin and was very big.

One fine, sunny morning, Kerbau Hitam decided to go ashore to steal what he could from the Raja of Riau. The pirates disguised themselves as merchants from Johor. When they came close to the shore, the Raja's men called out to them. "Who are you, and where do you come from?" "We are traders from Johor," Kerbau Hitam shouted. "We have some batik cloth and fine clothes that we would like to sell."

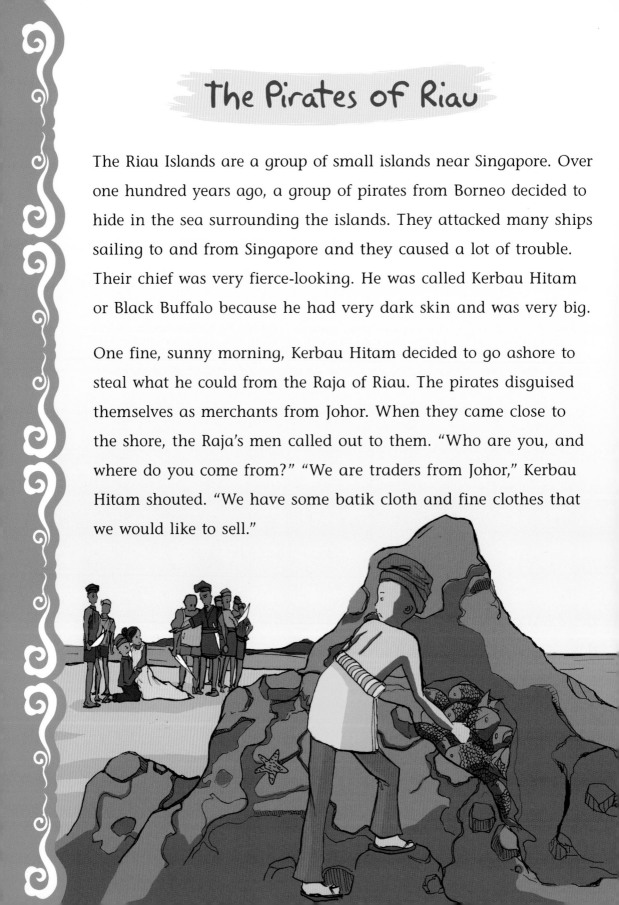

As it happened, the Raja's daughter, Normah, was looking for some new clothes for her wedding as she was to be married the next month.

"Very well," the raja said. "You can come ashore."

The pirates landed with their weapons hidden under their shirts. In a flash, they seized the raja and pressed a knife against his throat.

Kerbau Hitam called out to the villagers who were watching, "If you try to come closer, we shall kill your raja." All the villagers were then locked up in a store behind the raja's house. The raja was bound with rope and taken back to his house. His daughter tried to run away from the back of the house but she was caught by Kerbau Hitam. "I'm looking for a wife," he said. "You are a very pretty girl. Would you like to marry me?"

Normah screamed loudly and tried to escape. Kerbau Hitam ordered her to be tied up with her father. "She'll soon change her mind after she has had nothing but rice and water for a few days," he said.

However, the pirates did not know that Rahim, a fisherman, who was going to marry Normah, was watching them. He had been mending some fishing nets near the shore when the pirates landed. Without waiting a second, he jumped into his boat and sailed for Singapore. It was fortunate that the pirates were so busy that they did not notice him. He landed at Tanjong Rhu in Singapore. He was soon surrounded by a group of villagers. When he told them what had happened, they said, "You'd better come with us straight away to see our leader, the Temenggong. He will be able to help you."

When the Temenggong heard Rahim's report, he exclaimed, "It's terrible. The pirates must be stopped. I think I shall ask some of our Chinese friends to help us." He sent for the Chinese headman and discussed a plan with him.

Before dawn the next morning, a Chinese junk left Singapore for Riau. The Temenggong and some of his men, Rahim, and the Chinese leader, with twenty of his men, were on board. When they arrived at Riau, the Chinese headman shouted out to the pirates who were guarding the beach, "Can I speak to your raja?"

Kerbau Hitam came forward. "I am the raja," he said. "What do you want?"

"We are on the way to Singapore from China. One of my officers died at sea, and we would like to bury him at a famous Chinese temple on this island. Don't worry about money. We have plenty of gold on board. If you can allow us to land, I shall give you a big reward."

Kerbau Hitam answered, "Oh, all right. But you must come ashore with all your men. My men will guard your ship and the gold."

The Chinese headman rowed ashore in a boat, with ten of his followers, the Temenggong and his men, and Rahim. They were carrying a coffin. When they landed, they carried the coffin on their shoulders and walked towards a nearby Chinese temple.

"Stop!" ordered Kerbau Hitam. "Are you carrying any weapons?"

"We are merchants," said the Chinese headman. But Kerbau Hitam ordered them to be searched. No weapons were found.

Kerbau Hitam and his bodyguard quickly jumped into a boat and rowed out to the Chinese junk. They did not know that the rest of the Chinese headman's followers were hiding in the junk waiting for them to come. Before Kerbau Hitam knew what had happened, they were seized by the Chinese and locked in the hold of the junk.

By this time, the funeral procession had reached the Chinese temple. The coffin was placed on the ground. "Now!" shouted the Temenggong. In a flash, the men opened the coffin and took out the guns, swords and knives that had been hidden inside.

They ran to the raja's house, led by Rahim and the Temenggong, where the remaining pirates were easily captured after a short fight.

"You saved us just in time," the raja said. "They were just going to kill me, and Kerbau Hitam was going to force my daughter to marry him."

Rahim rushed towards Normah and untied her. He then set free the villagers who had been locked in the store at the back of the raja's house.

Rahim and Normah decided to get married immediately.

The raja thanked the Temenggong, the Chinese headman, and their men for saving his life. He invited them all to a big feast that evening to celebrate Rahim and Normah's wedding.

The next day, the Temenggong and the Chinese sailed back to Singapore taking Kerbau Hitam and his pirates with them. The pirates and their leader were tried and sent to prison for many years.